Read Multiply to find the product.

7 x 2	3 x 4	6 x 5	9 x 1	4 x 7	6 x 3
8 x 5	9 x 3	4 x 5	6 x 6	8 x 9	0 x 7
5 x 3	3 x 7	6 x 7	8 x 8	2 x 9	7 x 7
4 x 9	5 x 5	4 x 6	9 x 9	8 x 6	8 x 7
6 x 9	7 x 1	3 x 0	7 x 6	6 x 2	8 x 4
4 x 2	9 x 5	7 x 9	7 x 7	2 x 3	6 x 8

1

Read How fast can you solve these problems? Time yourself or ask someone to time you.

4 x 5	8 x 2	2 x 4	7 x 7	8 x 9	6 x 3
5 x 9	8 x 7	1 x 5	3 x 9	5 x 2	0 x 9
7 x 6	3 x 8	6 x 6	9 x 6	6 x 5	8 x 4
2 x 3	9 x 9	8 x 6	4 x 4	7 x 8	5 x 7
6 x 1	4 x 3	5 x 6	4 x 9	5 x 3	7 x 4
9 x 7	6 x 4	2 x 9	7 x 3	8 x 8	5 x 5

Time: _____

Read Read each problem and solve it. Show your work.

1. On Saturday, the pumpkin patch had a fill-the-bag sale! Seven people bought bags of nine small pumpkins each. How many small pumpkins were sold?

2. Eight people bought bags of six medium-sized pumpkins each. How many medium-sized pumpkins were sold?

3. Six people bought two bags of three large pumpkins each. How many large pumpkins were sold?

4. Pumpkins without stems were sold nine in a batch for a dollar. A baker bought nine batches of those pumpkins to make pies. How many pumpkins did he buy?

Bonus Challenge Problems

Level 1: How many pumpkins would be double the total number sold?

Level 2: How many would be twelve times the total number sold?

3

Read Solve each problem. Multiply the 1s column, then the 10s column.

```
 10 1
  2 1
x   3
─────
  6 3
```

```
  4 2
x   2
─────
```

```
  1 1
x   5
─────
```

```
  1 2
x   4
─────
```

```
  1 0
x   6
─────
```

```
  3 3
x   2
─────
```

```
  4 9
x   1
─────
```

```
  2 2
x   4
─────
```

```
  1 1
x   9
─────
```

```
  4 3
x   2
─────
```

```
  3 4
x   2
─────
```

```
  1 2
x   3
─────
```

```
  7 9
x   1
─────
```

```
  1 0
x   4
─────
```

```
  1 1
x   8
─────
```

```
  4 4
x   2
─────
```

```
  1 2
x   2
─────
```

```
  1 4
x   2
─────
```

```
  1 3
x   3
─────
```

```
  6 8
x   1
─────
```

```
  9 8
x   1
─────
```

```
  1 1
x   7
─────
```

```
  1 0
x   9
─────
```

```
  3 2
x   3
─────
```

Step 1

100	10	1
	3	
	2	⑥
x		⑥
		6

Step 2

100	10	1
	1	3
	②	6
x		⑥
	5	6

Step 3

100	10	1
	1	3
	2	6
x		6
1	5	6

Read Multiply to find the product. Regroup if you need to.

11
22
x 5
‾‾‾
110

16
x 3
‾‾‾

12
x 4
‾‾‾

17
x 7
‾‾‾

15
x 9
‾‾‾

12
x 9
‾‾‾

13
x 6
‾‾‾

19
x 5
‾‾‾

14
x 3
‾‾‾

11
x 8
‾‾‾

19
x 9
‾‾‾

10
x 8
‾‾‾

14
x 6
‾‾‾

15
x 4
‾‾‾

10
x 7
‾‾‾

Okay, okay! Time to regroup and figure out that play!

coach

5

Read Read each problem and solve it. Show your work.

1. During the candy sale, Peter sold 15 bags of giant gummy worms. Each bag held eight gummy worms. How many gummy worms did Peter sell?

2. Alyssa sold six boxes of banana flavored gumballs. Each box held 24 gumballs. How many gumballs did Alyssa sell?

3. Jamal sold 42 small boxes of chocolates. Each box held seven chocolates. How many chocolates did Jamal sell?

4. Mae Ling sold 34 bags of taffy. Each bag held nine pieces. How many pieces of taffy did Mae Ling sell?

Bonus Challenge Problems

Level 1: If three times as many bags and boxes of candy and gum were sold, how many bags and boxes would have been sold altogether?

Level 2: If four times as many pieces of candy and gum were sold, how many pieces would have been sold altogether?

Be Product-ive!

Multiply. Circle the smallest product and draw a box around the largest product.

32 x 9	16 x 8	22 x 6	17 x 4	45 x 7
12 x 5	13 x 3	19 x 1	12 x 7	11 x 9
19 x 9	20 x 6	14 x 5	15 x 4	30 x 8
37 x 3	11 x 2	24 x 6	42 x 7	17 x 2
25 x 6	36 x 9	28 x 2	49 x 1	36 x 7

Jars in a Row

 Read Multiply. Color the jar if the equation has an even-numbered product.

23 x 3	14 x 4	26 x 6	45 x 7	37 x 2
35 x 5	57 x 7	48 x 6	85 x 4	33 x 9
46 x 3	69 x 2	74 x 6	37 x 8	58 x 2
75 x 3	43 x 8	38 x 5	26 x 7	59 x 3

Read ▷ Divide to find the quotient.

Uh-oh!
Time to split!

$6\overline{)48}$ $3\overline{)27}$ $9\overline{)45}$ $4\overline{)36}$ $7\overline{)49}$

$54 \div 6 =$ $72 \div 8 =$ $42 \div 7 =$

$8\overline{)64}$ $6\overline{)36}$ $3\overline{)24}$ $2\overline{)14}$ $8\overline{)56}$

$63 \div 9 =$ $45 \div 5 =$ $81 \div 9 =$

$3\overline{)15}$ $7\overline{)35}$ $9\overline{)54}$ $6\overline{)42}$ $8\overline{)32}$

$6 \div 6 =$ $24 \div 4 =$ $21 \div 7 =$

Go for the Speed!

Read How fast can you solve these problems? Time yourself or ask someone to time you.

6⟌54	4⟌32	8⟌56	3⟌27	8⟌32	4⟌28
2⟌14	9⟌81	2⟌8	7⟌42	1⟌5	9⟌72
5⟌40	8⟌64	7⟌49	3⟌18	4⟌36	5⟌15
3⟌0	6⟌48	5⟌20	1⟌9	9⟌54	8⟌40
9⟌63	8⟌16	8⟌72	4⟌28	7⟌56	7⟌28
9⟌45	6⟌6	8⟌24	9⟌27	3⟌21	6⟌36

Time: _____

 Read Read each problem and solve it. Show your work.

1. During the two-hour "Music Madness" sale at the music store, one salesman sold $72 worth of CDs. He sold eight CDs in all. How much was each CD?

2. The salesman sold $54 worth of audio casettes. Each cassette costs $6. How many did he sell?

3. He sold seven posters for a total of $49. How much was each poster?

4. He sold nine CD singles for a total of $45. How much was each CD single?

Bonus Challenge Problems

Level 1: The manager was pleased with the amount of money the salesman made for the store. He only expected him to sell half of that amount. How much money did the manager expect the salesman to make for the store during the sale?

Level 2: If the salesman receives 10% of the total amount of sales he made, how much money will he get?

Sometimes a dividend cannot be divided evenly by a divisor. When that happens, a remainder is left.

$$\begin{array}{r} 6\ r\ 1 \\ 7\overline{)43} \\ 42 \\ \hline 1 \end{array}$$

Read Divide to find the answer. Write r for remainder.

$6\overline{)32}$ $8\overline{)47}$ $2\overline{)17}$ $7\overline{)38}$ $8\overline{)63}$

$6\overline{)45}$ $5\overline{)49}$ $2\overline{)19}$ $9\overline{)46}$ $5\overline{)31}$

$4\overline{)30}$ $8\overline{)44}$ $7\overline{)57}$ $2\overline{)15}$ $6\overline{)50}$

$9\overline{)80}$ $3\overline{)25}$ $5\overline{)42}$ $4\overline{)27}$ $8\overline{)58}$

What's Left Over?

Read Divide to find the answer. Circle the problem if there's a remainder.

The only thing worse than liver is leftover liver.

$6\overline{)54}$ $\qquad$ $4\overline{)25}$ $\qquad$ $8\overline{)56}$ $\qquad$ $3\overline{)22}$ $\qquad$ $4\overline{)31}$

$2\overline{)8}$ $\qquad$ $7\overline{)42}$ $\qquad$ $6\overline{)53}$ $\qquad$ $5\overline{)40}$ $\qquad$ $3\overline{)18}$

$4\overline{)34}$ $\qquad$ $5\overline{)17}$ $\qquad$ $8\overline{)49}$ $\qquad$ $4\overline{)28}$ $\qquad$ $2\overline{)13}$

$9\overline{)71}$ $\qquad$ $1\overline{)5}$ $\qquad$ $6\overline{)40}$ $\qquad$ $9\overline{)72}$ $\qquad$ $4\overline{)36}$

$5\overline{)15}$ $\qquad$ $7\overline{)60}$ $\qquad$ $8\overline{)37}$ $\qquad$ $6\overline{)19}$ $\qquad$ $2\overline{)17}$

Read Divide to find the answer.

```
    14
6 ⌐84      7 ⌐91      8 ⌐88      3 ⌐66      5 ⌐85
   ↓
   6
  24
  24
```

2 ⌐24   7 ⌐84   6 ⌐72   3 ⌐84   2 ⌐36

5 ⌐60   4 ⌐56   3 ⌐42   6 ⌐78   8 ⌐96

Six containers of raspberry-chocolate-peanut ice cream hold 96 single scoops altogether. How many single scoops does one container hold?

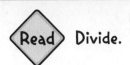 **Read** Divide.

$3\overline{)63}$ $7\overline{)98}$ $9\overline{)90}$ $4\overline{)84}$ $4\overline{)60}$

$8\overline{)88}$ $5\overline{)70}$ $7\overline{)77}$ $2\overline{)28}$ $3\overline{)93}$

$7\overline{)91}$ $3\overline{)36}$ $2\overline{)62}$ $5\overline{)95}$ $4\overline{)92}$

If there are 96 ounces of orange juice in the
pitcher, how many 8-ounce glasses can be filled?

Bonus Challenge Problems

Level 1: How many 12-ounce glasses of orange juice can be filled?

Level 2: How many 3-ounce glasses can be filled from three
pitchers of juice?

Read Divide. Circle the problems with a remainder of 4.

```
   15 r2        10 r7
6)92         9)97         5)56         7)85         2)75
  ↓            ↓
  6            9
  32           7
  30
   2
```

```
3)94         3)77         6)87         2)79         3)82
```

```
7)86         5)84         3)74         6)98         6)93
```

```
5)97         7)99         4)85         8)92         9)94
```

Read Solve the problems. Then use the code to solve the riddle.

What kind of tree did the math professor plant?

Letter Code:

r 1 = r	r 4 = g	r 7 = t
r 2 = a	r 5 = o	r 8 = y
r 3 = e	r 6 = m	

5)57	9)94	7)73	6)41

9)42	4)27	8)63	7)22	9)80

seeds

17

To multiply a three-digit number by a one-digit number, multiply the 1s first, then the 10s, and then the 100s.

$$\begin{array}{r} 431 \\ \times\ 2 \\ \hline 2 \end{array} \qquad \begin{array}{r} 431 \\ \times\ 2 \\ \hline 62 \end{array} \qquad \begin{array}{r} 431 \\ \times\ 2 \\ \hline 862 \end{array}$$

- -

 Multiply to find the product.

$$\begin{array}{r} 303 \\ \times\ 3 \end{array} \qquad \begin{array}{r} 112 \\ \times\ 4 \end{array} \qquad \begin{array}{r} 223 \\ \times\ 2 \end{array} \qquad \begin{array}{r} 430 \\ \times\ 2 \end{array}$$

 Multiply. Regroup as needed.

$$\begin{array}{r} \overset{111}{445} \\ \times\ 3 \\ \hline 1{,}335 \end{array} \qquad \begin{array}{r} 500 \\ \times\ 6 \end{array} \qquad \begin{array}{r} 727 \\ \times\ 4 \end{array}$$

$$\begin{array}{r} 594 \\ \times\ 3 \end{array} \qquad \begin{array}{r} 216 \\ \times\ 8 \end{array} \qquad \begin{array}{r} 987 \\ \times\ 4 \end{array}$$

Read Read each problem and solve it using addition and multiplication.

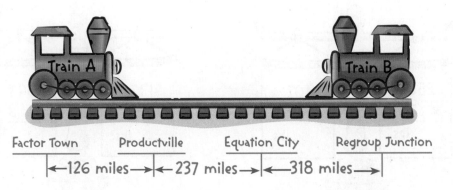

Factor Town   Productville   Equation City   Regroup Junction

←126 miles→←237 miles→←318 miles→

1. Train B made a round trip (there and back) from Regroup Junction to Equation City. How many miles did it travel?

2. Train A made two round trips between Productville and Equation City. How many miles did it travel?

3. Train A made five round trips between Factor Town and Productville. How many miles did it travel?

Bonus Challenge Problems

Level 1: How many miles are five round trips between Factor Town and Regroup Junction?

Level 2: How many combined miles are three round trips between Factor Town and Equation City and two round trips between Productville and Regroup Junction?

Heavy Math

Read Multiply. Circle the problem with the "heaviest" quotient in each pair.

256
x 7
_____ lbs.

807
x 2
_____ lbs.

432
x 5
_____ lbs.

649
x 3
_____ lbs.

429
x 3
_____ lbs.

714
x 5
_____ lbs.

902
x 7
_____ lbs.

568
x 5
_____ lbs.

778
x 3
_____ lbs.

212
x 6
_____ lbs.

594
x 4
_____ lbs.

327
x 8
_____ lbs.

Now you're ready to divide a three-digit number by a one-digit number.

```
    1              13             130
5 650          5 650          5 650
  5              5              5
  1             15             15
                15             15
                 0             00
```

◇ Read ◇ Divide to find the quotient.

4 720   6 648   7 777   5 725

3 396   9 981   8 864   6 846

2 246   5 955   4 564   7 917

Sometimes the divisor will be larger than the digit in the 100s place of the dividend. When this happens, the quotient will be less than 100.

```
      5              54
  6)324          6)324
    30              30↓
     2              24
                    24
```

 Divide to find the quotient.

4)348   5)405   9)477   6)366

3)126   7)574   8)352   2)174

6)468   5)250   9)378   7)644

Read Divide. Then use the code to solve the riddle.

Letter Code:

101 = F	305 = I
103 = a	401 = d
107 = y	

What is an insect's favorite weekday?

		—
5)505	3)915	4)428
2)802	1)103	3)321

Sssssolve It!

Read ⟩ Divide. Write r for remainder.

Ssssome of the problemsssss will have remaindersssssss!

2⟌468   3⟌173   2⟌816   7⟌899

5⟌427   8⟌984   8⟌672   5⟌244

3⟌303   8⟌400   2⟌106   9⟌983

5⟌659   6⟌385   7⟌742   8⟌513

Read Read each problem and solve it using division.

1. The corner store sold 875 comic books in one week. If it sold the same number of comic books each day, how many were sold in one day?

2. The store also sold 230 packs of trading cards in three days. On the first two days, it sold the same number of card packs. But on the third day it sold two more. How many packs of cards were sold the first two days? How many were sold on the third day?

3. The store made $306 from posters that week. If the price of each poster was $9, how many posters were sold?

COMICS

POSTERS

TRADING CARDS

Bonus Challenge Problems

Level 1: The store owner ordered another 2,550 comic books. The books come in small boxes of six each. How many boxes will the store owner receive?

Level 2: The owner also ordered 1,032 new packs of trading cards. If there are 24 packs to a carton, how many cartons will the store owner receive?

To multiply a two-digit number by a two-digit number, follow these steps.

First, multiply 24 by 2 ones.

```
  24
x 12
----
  48
```

Then, multiply 24 by 1 ten.

```
  24
x 12
----
  48
  24
```

Add the two rows of answers.

```
  24
x 12
----
  48
  24
----
 288
```

First multiply by me.

Then multiply by me!

And don't forget to use me to add the answer rows!

◇ Read ⟩ Multiply.

```
  38        41        31        33
x 11      x 12      x 31      x 22
```

```
  44        21        62        13
x 20      x 14      x 11      x 12
```

Remember to regroup.

37 x 2 ones   37 x 4 tens   Add the 2 answer rows.

```
                        12                 12
   1                 1                  1
  37                37                 37
x 42              x 42               x 42
  74                74                 74
                   148                148
                                     1554
```

◇ Read ▷ **Multiply.**

```
   25            43            37            52
 x 55          x 20          x 31          x 29
```

```
   38            36            31            42
 x 73          x 24          x 23          x 29
```

If Ann eats 38 peanuts every day, how many does she eat in three weeks?

Read Multiply. Then use the code to solve the riddle.

Letter Code:

672 = a	1,342 = s
1,312 = c	1,242 = t
1,440 = e	1,536 = w
945 = h	

Why did the math teacher make the big cat sit next to her during the test?

Because...

27 x 35	36 x 40		48 x 32	16 x 42	61 x 22		48 x 14

82 x 16	63 x 15	72 x 20	96 x 15	54 x 23	32 x 21	21 x 45

Read Multiply.

54	43	37	50
x 17	x 35	x 94	x 48

59	61	34	28
x 22	x 42	x 25	x 73

32	16	97	44
x 32	x 89	x 21	x 36

71	39	99	74
x 42	x 56	x 41	x 23

Read Read each problem and solve it using multiplication.

1. Saturday at the farmer's market, 65 baskets of tomatoes were sold. Each basket held 24 tomatoes. How many tomatoes were sold in all?

2. A restaurant chef bought 47 bags of potatoes. Each bag held 36 potatoes. How many did the chef buy in all?

3. A baker bought 56 cartons of eggs. Each carton held 18 eggs. How many eggs did the baker buy in all?

Bonus Challenge Problems

Level 1: A local grocer bought 24 cases of green peppers, 20 cases of red peppers, 15 cases of yellow peppers, and 14 cases of orange peppers. Each case held 100 peppers. How many peppers did the grocer buy in all?

Level 2: The grocer buys that many peppers each week for 12 weeks in the summer. How many peppers does he buy in all during the summer?

To multiply a three-digit number by a two-digit number, follow these steps.

First, multiply
324 by 5 ones.

1 1 2
```
  324
x  35
 1620
```

Then, multiply
324 by 3 tens.

      1
1 1 2
```
  324
x  35
 1620
  972
```

Add the two
rows of answers.

      1
1 1 2
```
  3 24
x   35
 1620
  972
11340
```

◇ Read Multiply.

```
  123          421          632          437
x  31        x  25        x  30        x  29
```

```
  271          674          813          625
x  43        x  51        x  15        x  92
```

```
  924          363          123          245
x  18        x  86        x  45        x  62
```

Ahoy, Matey!

Read Multiply. Circle the
even-numbered products.

721 x 47	214 x 74	532 x 45	457 x 63
811 x 22	109 x 96	491 x 27	345 x 69
577 x 63	298 x 99	195 x 38	495 x 87
833 x 37	264 x 63	754 x 49	529 x 29

Read Complete the puzzle by solving the problems.

Across

1. 589
   x 26

3. 261
   x 12

4. 991
   x 82

Down

1. 632
   x 18

2. 241
   x 80

5. 742
   x 34

33

Read Read the story and answer the questions below. Show your work.

With the picnic nearby, the 213 ants of the Huge Anthill Under the Tree were busy. They each carried nine crumbs of bread back to their hill. Then, each of them carried 42 poppy seeds to the hill. Next, they each carried 36 grains of sugar. By that time, the ants were so exhausted that they each took a 55-minute nap.

How many of each did the ants carry in all?

Bread crumbs: Poppy seeds: Sugar grains:

_____   _____   _____

Bonus Challenge Problems

Level 1: How many total minutes did the ants nap together?

Level 2: Convert the minutes to hours and minutes.

When you write out the steps as you divide, it's called long division.

You can do it! Just take one step at a time!

```
      1 2 3 3
   8 )9 8 6 4
     8
     ─
     1 8
     1 6
     ──
       2 6
       2 4
       ──
         2 4
         2 4
         ──
```

```
      3 2 3
   4 )1 2 9 2
     1 2
     ──
        9
        8
        ─
        1 2
        1 2
        ──
```

Read Divide.

$$5)\overline{6555} \qquad 6)\overline{3372} \qquad 7)\overline{8428}$$

$$9)\overline{9081} \qquad 4)\overline{3992}$$

35

652r3

5871

Divide by 9!

Read ▷ Divide. Circle the problems with remainders.

```
    488 r5
7)3421        5)6643        3)2967        8)2896
  26
  62
  56
  61
  56
   5
```

```
2)6418        6)4446        4)1729        9)6102
```

A divisor larger than 9 calls for long division.

```
      12
  23)276
     23
     46
     46
```

```
      14r9
  32)457
     32
     137
     128
       9
```

```
       13
  28)369
     28
     89
     84
      5
```

- -

 Divide.

```
45)945
```

```
62)813
```

```
32)736
```

```
73)805
```

```
22)462
```

```
17)408
```

Read Divide. Circle the problems with odd-numbered remainders.

64⟌963   56⟌680   27⟌301

15⟌456   97⟌979   54⟌601

29⟌734   62⟌746   49⟌747

Do you have this in a size long?

TURTLENECK SALE!

38

Quotient Match-up

Divide to solve each problem. Then draw a line to the matching quotient.

16)560

20)720

27)999

19)722

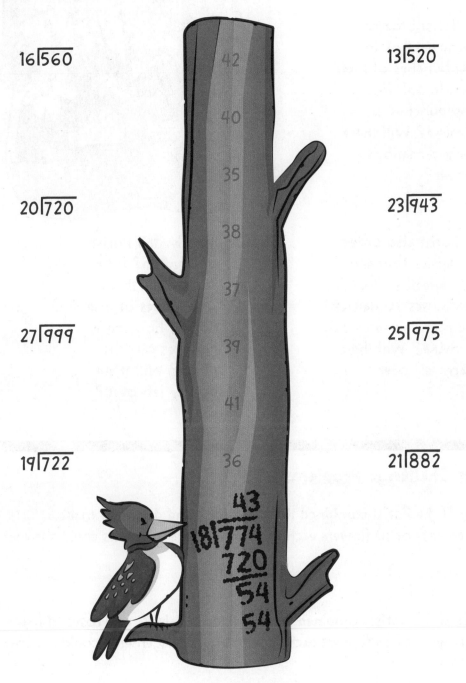

42

40

35

38

37

39

41

36

13)520

23)943

25)975

21)882

39

Read Read and solve each problem.

1. The florist ordered 728 carnations to make bunches of three dozen to sell. How many bunches can she make? Will there be any carnations left over?

2. The florist also ordered 912 daisies to make daisy wreaths. If each wreath uses 70 daisies, how many wreaths can she make? Will there be any left over?

3. Finally, the florist ordered 552 roses. If she sells them in bunches of one dozen, how many bunches can she make? Will there be any left over?

Bonus Challenge Problems

Level 1: If the florist combined the carnations and daisies to make arrangements of 10 flowers each, how many arrangements could she make?

Level 2: If the florist combined the carnations, daisies, and roses to make arrangements of 16 flowers each, how many arrangements could she make?

Third time's a charm!

Read▷ Divide. Circle the three problems with the same answer.

81)972   72)798   15)574   22)321

37)414   42)506   19)422   21)802

12)460   51)722   36)800   55)883

64 x 5 = 320 < 322
64 x 6 = 384 > 322

$$\begin{array}{r} 5\,r\,2 \\ 64\overline{)322} \\ 320 \\ \hline 2 \end{array}$$

The stronger your multiplication skills are, the stronger your division skills will be!

98 x 4 = 392 < 403
98 x 5 = 490 > 403

$$\begin{array}{r} 4\,r\,11 \\ 98\overline{)403} \\ 392 \\ \hline 11 \end{array}$$

Read Divide.

$$36\overline{)218} \qquad\qquad 56\overline{)351} \qquad\qquad 41\overline{)369}$$

$$92\overline{)744} \qquad\qquad 25\overline{)176} \qquad\qquad 12\overline{)119}$$

Read Divide to solve the problems. Then use the code to answer the question.

What's my favorite kind of cheese?

Letter Code:

3 = r	6 = u	9 = e
4 = s	7 = m	
5 = t	8 = n	

			-
86⟌602	98⟌588	63⟌567	72⟌576
86⟌344	51⟌255	58⟌522	74⟌222

43

Read Divide to find the answers. Then multiply to check your answers.

19⟌114   19 × ☐ ☐

36⟌324   36 × ☐ ☐

45⟌360   45 × ☐ ☐

74⟌518   74 × ☐ ☐

287 ÷ 63 = 4 r 35

Read Circle the problem with the largest remainder.

76⟌234   82⟌589   22⟌739

Read Solve each problem.

9 x 7 =   8⟌64   81 ÷ 9 =

```
  36
x  5
```
          5⟌90   8 x 7 =

9⟌225
```
 467
x  3
```
          8⟌432

```
 622
x  3
```
          94⟌568
```
 341
x 27
```

45

 Read Solve each problem.

```
   98
 x  7
```

```
3⟌138
```

```
   64
 x 24
```

```
7⟌28
```

```
2⟌460
```

```
  881
 x 11
```

```
4⟌648
```

```
  746
 x 13
```

```
45⟌378
```

A number multiplied by itself is the square root of the product. What is the square root of 256?

Read Read each problem. Then, multiply or divide to solve it.

1. Sid was given nine packs of 25 tickets each to sell for the school play. He sold the same amount each hour for six hours. How many did he sell each hour? How many did he have left over?

2. Anna sold popcorn during the play. She bought eight sacks of kernels that made 46 cups of popcorn each. She had exactly enough to sell 92 bags of popcorn. How many cups were in each bag?

3. Each night, 196 people came to see the play, which ran for three nights. One quarter of each audience was given aisle seats. How many people had aisle seats each night? How many had aisle seats altogether during the three nights?

Bonus Challenge Problems

Level 1: The tickets were $3 a piece. Given the amount of people that saw the play, how much money was made from all the ticket sales?

Level 2: The play cost $425 to put on. How much would 14 times the profit gained from all the ticket sales be?

Multiply Three by Three

First multiply
422 by 9 ones.

```
  3 1 1
  4 2 2
x 5 3 9
─────────
  3798
```

Then multiply
422 by 3 tens.

```
    1
  3 1 1
  4 2 2
x 5 3 9
─────────
  3798
  1266
```

Next, multiply
422 by 5 hundreds.

```
  2
  1
  3 1 1
  4 2 2
x 5 3 9
─────────
  3798
  1266
  2110
```

Add.

```
  2
  1
  3 1 1
  4 2 2
x 5 3 9
─────────
  3798
  1266
  2110
──────────
 227458
```

Read Multiply. Remember to regroup as needed.

```
  416          762          945
x 741        x 368        x 267
```

```
  539          498          809
x 733        x 612        x 532
```

```
  222
x 333
──────
73,926
```

```
  531
x 246
───────
130,626
```

 Read Maria rushed through her make-up test during recess so she'd have time to play outside. Solve each problem to see if Maria found the correct product. If she did not, circle your answer.

Maria's answer:
117,269

$$\begin{array}{r} 483 \\ \times\ 243 \\ \hline \end{array}$$

Maria's answer:
175,260

$$\begin{array}{r} 345 \\ \times\ 508 \\ \hline \end{array}$$

Maria's answer:
81,300

$$\begin{array}{r} 661 \\ \times\ 123 \\ \hline \end{array}$$

Maria's answer:
318,000

$$\begin{array}{r} 375 \\ \times\ 848 \\ \hline \end{array}$$

Maria's answer:
265,454

$$\begin{array}{r} 934 \\ \times\ 281 \\ \hline \end{array}$$

Maria's answer:
281,432

$$\begin{array}{r} 567 \\ \times\ 496 \\ \hline \end{array}$$

Read Read each problem and solve it.

1. The apple orchard has nine rows of green apple trees with 16 trees in each row. If each tree produces 542 apples, how many green apples will there be in all?

2. There are 22 rows of yellow apples with 31 trees in each row. If each tree produces 459 apples, how many yellow apples will there be in all?

3. There are 32 rows of red apples with 30 trees in each row. If each tree produces 612 apples, how many red apples will there be in all?

Multiply two different times for each problem!

Bonus Challenge Problems

Level 1: If there were 81 rows of green apple trees and each tree produced 542 apples, how many green apples would there be in all?

Level 2: If there were 412 red apple trees in each row and each produced 612 apples, how many would there be in all?

TOPIC	TOTAL
Science Books	749
History Books	814
Health Books	533
Cookbooks	278

 Read Use the information found on the Village Library book count printout to solve the problems.

1. If each science book was checked out 942 times, how many science book check-outs were there in all?

2. If each history book was checked out 587 times, how many history book check-outs were there in all?

3. If each health book was checked out 604 times, how many health book check-outs were there in all?

4. If each cookbook was checked out 836 times, how many cookbook check-outs were there in all?

GUESS HOW MANY

My quess is 2,985 X 462.

```
  221          441          3452
  4673         221          441          4673
 x 764        4673         221         x 764
 18692       x 764        4673         18692
             18692       x 764         28038
             28038       18692         32711
                         28038        3570172
                         32711
```

Read ▷ Multiply.

```
  8561         2163         9336
 x 654        x 749        x 293
```

```
  4637         7363
 x 273        x 747
```

Read Multiply. Circle the largest product and mark an X on the smallest product.

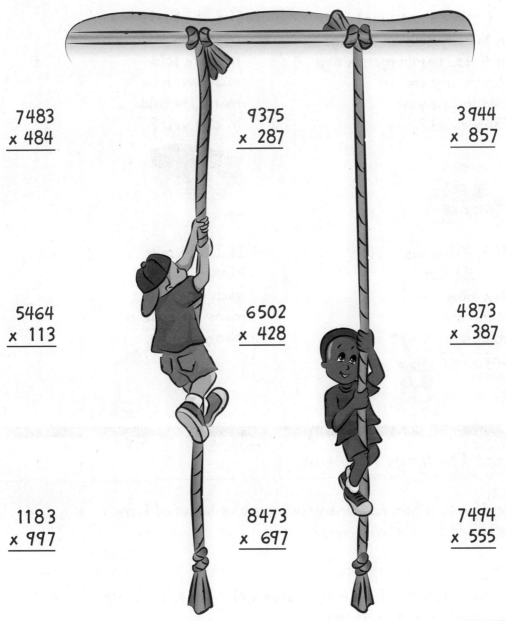

7483
x 484

9375
x 287

3944
x 857

5464
x 113

6502
x 428

4873
x 387

1183
x 997

8473
x 697

7494
x 555

Read Read each problem and multiply to solve it.

1. A fast food restaurant in the city sells an average of 4,432 hamburgers a day. How many are sold in one year (365 days)?

2. If 3,751 boxes of French fries are sold each day, how many are sold in one year?

3. If 5,703 sodas are sold each day, how many are sold in one year?

4. If 2,684 milk shakes are sold each day, how many are sold in two years?

Bonus Challenge Problems

Level 1: Altogether, how many burgers plus boxes of French fries would be sold in 3 years?

Level 2: Altogether, how many burgers plus boxes of French fries would be sold in 33 years?

Read Complete the puzzle by solving the problems.

Across:

1.	6549	4.	8211	5.	2121
	x 763		x 479		x 324

Down:

1.	9999	2.	6541	3.	2157
	x 444		x 922		x 352

55

$$\begin{array}{r} 241 \\ 23\overline{)5543} \\ \underline{46} \\ 94 \\ \underline{92} \\ 23 \\ \underline{23} \end{array}$$

$$\begin{array}{r} 55 \\ 34\overline{)1870} \\ \underline{170} \\ 170 \\ \underline{170} \end{array}$$

$$\begin{array}{r} 74\,r\,16 \\ 57\overline{)4234} \\ \underline{399} \\ 244 \\ \underline{228} \\ 16 \end{array}$$

"Follow these examples to conjure up some magical math!"

Read Divide.

$$26\overline{)7410} \qquad 39\overline{)2418} \qquad 50\overline{)3750}$$

$$76\overline{)8923} \qquad 34\overline{)4024} \qquad 85\overline{)5440}$$

Read Divide. Then circle the problems with remainders.

$$25\overline{)8000}$$ $$56\overline{)8742}$$ $$60\overline{)1860}$$

$$48\overline{)1700}$$ $$11\overline{)2981}$$ $$90\overline{)7210}$$

$$15\overline{)6045}$$ $$34\overline{)3298}$$ $$75\overline{)6375}$$

Read Read each problem and divide to solve it.

1. If a small aircraft flew 2,079 miles in 11 hours, how many miles would it have to travel each hour?

2. If the same aircraft flew 4,080 miles at 170 miles per hour, how many hours would the flight take?

3. If a large passenger plane flew 8,730 miles in 18 hours, how many miles would it have to travel each hour?

4. If the same passenger plane flew 3,144 miles at 524 miles per hour, how many hours would the flight take?

Bonus Challenge Problems

Level 1: If a large passenger plane flew 13,920 miles in 24 hours, how many miles would it have to travel each hour?

Level 2: A small aircraft pilot logged in 265,200 flight miles over 156 round trips to and from the same destination. What would the one-way mileage be? What would the round trip mileage be?

Read Solve each problem using multiplication or division. Then draw lines to match the quotients and products.

9⟌5670

$\begin{array}{r} 17 \\ \times\ \ 5 \\ \hline \end{array}$

23⟌1955

$\begin{array}{r} 61 \\ \times\ \ 6 \\ \hline \end{array}$

18⟌8190

$\begin{array}{r} 72 \\ \times\ \ 4 \\ \hline \end{array}$

26⟌9516

$\begin{array}{r} 70 \\ \times\ \ 9 \\ \hline \end{array}$

34⟌9792

$\begin{array}{r} 35 \\ \times\ 13 \\ \hline \end{array}$

Read Write your name on the line.
Then solve the problems and use the code to finish the sentence.

Letter Code:

48 = m	73 = e	1122 = a	20,904 = s
49 = i	259 = t	1969 = h	640,095 = r

_____

Name

35⟌1715	871 x 24	2⟌2244

48⟌2304	51 x 22	38⟌9842	5⟌9845

67⟌3216	102 x 11	1742 x 12	21⟌5439	56⟌4088	1535 x 417

!

page 1

14	12	30	9	28	18
40	27	20	36	72	0
15	21	42	64	18	49
36	25	24	81	48	56
54	7	0	42	12	32
8	45	63	49	6	48

page 2

20	16	8	49	72	18
45	56	5	27	10	0
42	24	36	54	30	32
6	81	48	16	56	35
6	12	30	36	15	28
63	24	18	21	64	25

page 3

1. 63 small pumpkins
2. 48 medium-sized pumpkins
3. 36 large pumpkins
4. 81 pumpkins without stems
CL1: 456 pumpkins
CL2: 2,736 pumpkins

page 4

63	84	55	48
60	66	49	88
99	86	68	36
79	40	88	88
24	28	39	68
98	77	90	96

page 5

110	48	48	119	135
108	78	95	42	88
171	80	84	60	70

page 6

1. 120 gummy worms
2. 144 gumballs
3. 294 chocolates
4. 306 pieces
CL1: 291 bags and boxes
CL2: 3,456 pieces

page 7

288	128	132	68	315
60	39	(19)	84	99
171	120	70	60	240
111	22	144	294	34
150	[324]	56	49	252

page 8

69	56	156	315	74
175	399	288	340	297
138	138	444	296	116
225	344	190	182	177

page 9

8	9	5	9	7
9	9	6		
8	6	8	7	7
7	9	9		
5	5	6	7	4
1	6	3		

page 10

9	8	7	9	4	7
7	9	4	6	5	8
8	8	7	6	9	3
0	8	4	9	6	5
7	2	9	7	8	4
5	1	3	3	7	6

page 11

1. $9
2. 9 cassettes
3. $7
4. $5
CL1: $110
CL2: $22

page 12

5r2	5r7	8r1	5r3	7r7
7r3	9r4	9r1	5r1	6r1
7r2	5r4	8r1	7r1	8r2
8r8	8r1	8r2	6r3	7r2

page 13

9	(6r1)	7	(7r1)	(7r3)
4	6	(8r5)	8	6
(8r2)	(3r2)	(6r1)	7	(6r1)
(7r8)	5	(6r4)	8	9
3	(8r4)	(4r5)	(3r1)	(8r1)

page 14

14	13	11	22	17
12	12	12	28	18
12	14	14	13	12

16 scoops

page 15

21	14	10	21	15
11	14	11	14	31
13	12	31	19	23

12 glasses
CL1: 8 glasses
CL2: 96 glasses

Answer Key

page 16

15r2 10r7 11r1 12r1 37r1
31r1 25r2 14r3 39r1 27r1
12r2 (16r4) 24r2 16r2 15r3
19r2 14r1 21r1 (11r4) (10r4)

page 17

a geometry

11r2 • 10r4 10r3 6r5 -
4r6 6r3 7r7 3r1 8r8

page 18

909   448   446   860

1,335   3,000 2,908
1,782   1,728 3,948

page 19

636 miles
948 miles
1,260 miles
CL1: 6,810 miles
CL2: 4,398 miles

page 20

(1,792) 1,614   (2,160) 1,947
1,287 (3,570) (6,314) 2,840
(2,334) 1,272 2,376 (2,616)

page 21

180 108 111 145
132 109 108 141
123 191 141 131

page 22

87 81 53 61
42 82 44 87
78 50 42 92

page 23

Flyday
101 305 107 —
401 103 107

page 24

234   57r2   408 128r3
85r2   123   84   48r4
101   50   53 109r2
131r4 64r1 106 64r1

page 25

1. 125 comic books
2. 76 packs the first two days;
   78 packs the third day
3. 34 posters
CL1: 425 boxes
CL2: 43 cartons

page 26

418 492 961 726
880 294 682 156

page 27

1,375   860 1,147 1,508
2,774   864   713 1,218

798 peanuts

page 28

Because...he was a cheetah
945 1,440 • 1,536 672 1,342 • 672 •
1,312 945 1,440 1,440 1,242 672 945

page 29

918   1,505 3,478 2,400
1,298 2,562   850 2,044
1,024 1,424 2,037 1,584
2,982 2,184 4,059 1,702

page 30

1. 1,560 tomatoes
2. 1,692 potatoes
3. 1,008 eggs
CL1: 7,300 peppers
CL2: 87,600 peppers

page 31

3,813	10,525	18,960	12,673
11,653	34,374	12,195	57,500
16,632	31,218	5,535	15,190

page 32

33,887	(15,836)	(23,940)	28,791
(17,842)	(10,464)	13,257	23,805
36,351	(29,502)	(7,410)	43,065
30,821	(16,632)	(36,946)	15,341

page 33

¹·1	5	3	²·1	4		
1			9			
³·3	1	3	2			
7		⁴·8	1	2	6	⁵·2
6			0			5
						2
						2
						8

page 34

Bread crumbs: 1,917

Poppy Seeds: 8,946

Sugar grains: 7,668

CL1: 11,715 minutes

CL2: 195 hours and
15 minutes

page 35

1,311	562	1,204
	1,009	998

page 36

(488r5)	(1,328r3)	989
362	3,209	741
(432r1)	678	

page 37

21	13r7	23
11r2	21	24

page 38

(15r3)	12r8	11r4
30r6	(10r9)	(11r7)
(25r9)	12r2	15r12

page 39

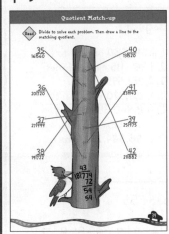

Quotient Match-up

page 40

1. 20 bunches; 8 carnations left over
2. 13 wreaths; 2 daisies left over
3. 46 bunches; 0 roses left over

CL1: 164 arrangements

CL2: 137 arrangements

page 41

12	11r6	(38r4)	14r13
11r7	12r2	22r4	(38r4)
(38r4)	14r8	22r8	16r3

page 42

6r2	6r15	9
8r8	7r1	9r11

page 43

muenster

7	6	9	8-
4	5	9	3

page 44

page 45

63	8	9
180	18	56
25	1,401	54
1,866	6r4	9,207

page 46

686	46	1,536
4	230	9,691
162	9,698	8r18

16 (square root of 256)

page 47

1. 37 tickets; 3 left over
2. 4 cups
3. 49 each night; 147 all together

CL1: $1,764

CL2: $18,746

page 48

308,256	280,416	252,315
395,087	304,776	430,388

page 49

(117,369)	175,260	(81,303)
318,000	(262,454)	(281,232)

page 50

1. 78,048 green apples
2. 313,038 yellow apples
3. 587,520 red apples

CL1: 702,432 green apples

CL2: 8,068,608 red apples

page 51

1. 705,558 science book check-outs
2. 477,818 history book check-outs
3. 321,932 health book check-outs
4. 232,408 cookbook check-outs

page 52

5,598,894

1,620,087

2,735,448

1,265,901

5,500,161

page 53

3,621,772	2,690,625	3,380,008
~~617,432~~	2,782,856	1,885,851,
1,179,451	(5,905,681)	4,159,170

page 54

1. 1,617,680 hamburgers
2. 1,369,115 boxes of fries
3. 2,081,595 sodas
4. 1,959,320 milk shakes

CL1: 8,960,385 burgers and boxes of fries

CL2: 98,564,235 burgers and boxes of fries

page 55

¹.4	9	9	².6	8	8	³.7	
4			0			5	
⁴.3	9	3	3	0	6	9	
9			0			2	
5			8			6	
5			0			4	
⁵.6	8	7	2	0	4		

page 56

285	62	75
117r31	118r12	64

page 57

320	(156r6)	31
(35r20)	271	(80r10)
403	97	85

page 58

1. 189 miles
2. 24 hours
3. 485 miles
4. 6 hours

CL1: 580 miles

CL2: 850 miles one way
1,700 miles round trip

page 59

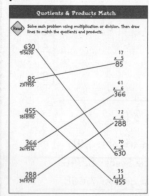

page 60

(your name) is a math master!

49	20,904	• 1,122 •	
48	1,122	259	1,969
48	1,122	20,904	—
259	73	640,095	